Christmas Ornaments

to cut out, color, and hang on your tree!

by Jo-Anne Metsch Bonnell

tempo books

GROSSET & DUNLAP
A FILMWAYS COMPANY
PUBLISHERS   NEW YORK

Now you can make your very own Christmas ornaments! All you need are scissors, crayons, paste, and string. You may want to add glitter or use paint instead of crayons. Or you might paste cotton on Santa's beard and the angel's hair. It's up to you!

Here are some things to remember. Fold on dashed ____lines. Cut out solid ● black circles to tie string through. Small diagrams will help you to see what the finished ornament will look like. Always color the ornaments before cutting them out. Just follow the instructions and see how beautiful you can make your Christmas tree!

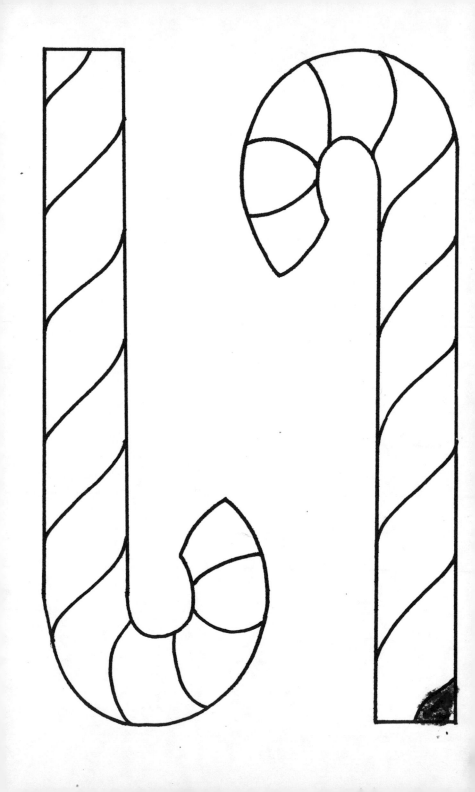

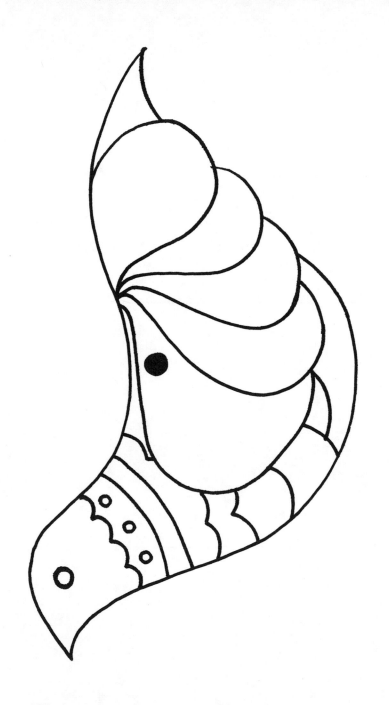

How to make the Rocking Horse on the next page

1. Fold tab down on package and paste to inside of opposite package.
2. Fold tabs down on rocker. Paste to inside of opposite rocker.
3. Tie string through opening in package.
4. Your rocking horse will look like this

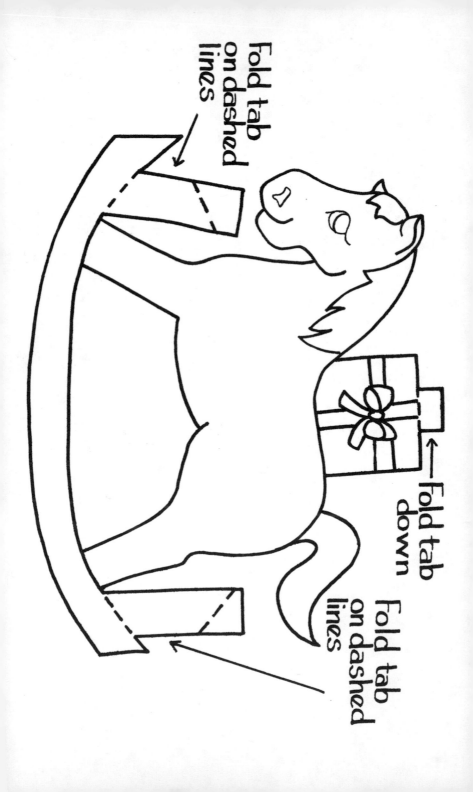

Fold tab on dashed lines

Fold tab down

Fold tab on dashed lines

Christmas Tree

1. Fold this tree on the dashed line.

2. Fold the tree on the next page on the dashed line.

3. Paste the back of the folds together as shown in the picture on the next page.

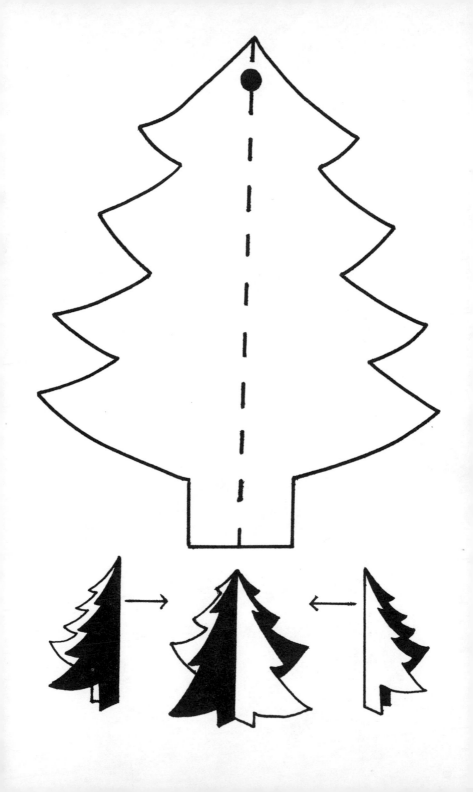

How to make the
Star

1. Fold the stars on the dashed lines.

2. Paste the back of the folds together as shown.

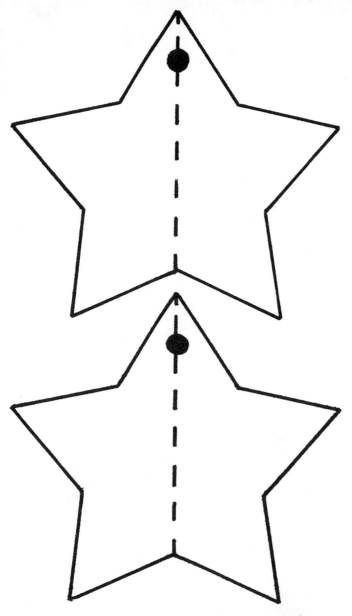

Your star will look
like this ⟶

Christmas Bell

1. Fold bells on the dashed lines.
2. Paste the back of the folds

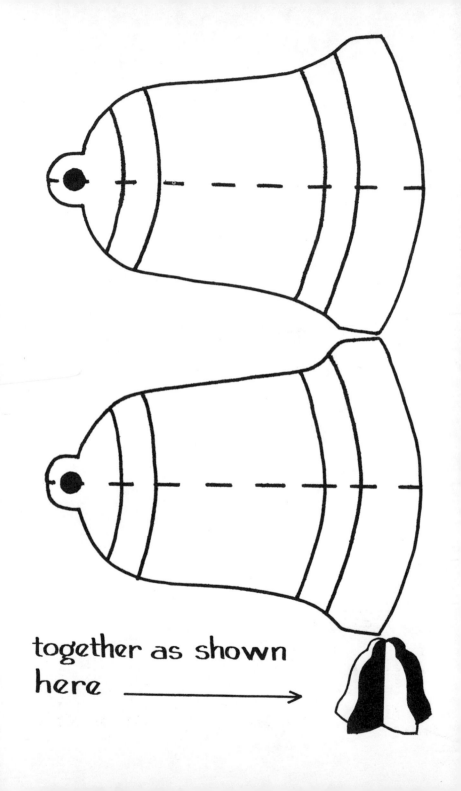

together as shown
here ————————→

How to make the Angel
on the next page

1. Roll angel's gown into cone shape. Paste tabs to inside.
2. Fold head on dashed line.
3. Paste tabs to inside of cone.
4. Paste halo to back of head.
5. Paste wings to back.
6. Your angel will look like this

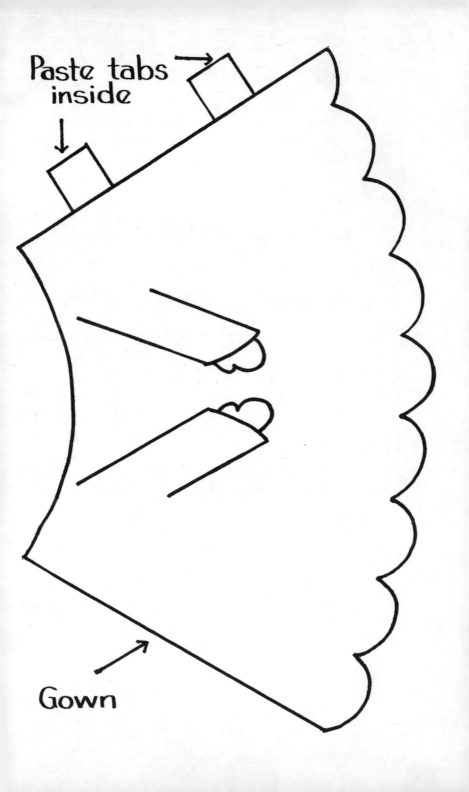

Paste tabs inside

Gown

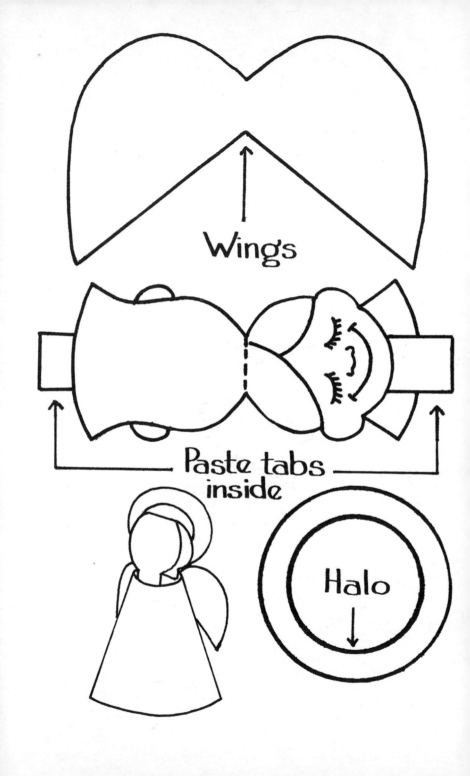

Wings

Paste tabs
inside

Halo

How to make the
Carolers
on the next pages

1. Roll caroler's robe into cone shape. Paste tabs to inside.

2. Fold head on dashed line. Paste tabs to inside of cone.

3. Cut slots on heavy lines between the hands.

4. Fold book on dashed line and insert into slots.

5. Paste bow onto cone.

6. Your caroler will look like this ⟶

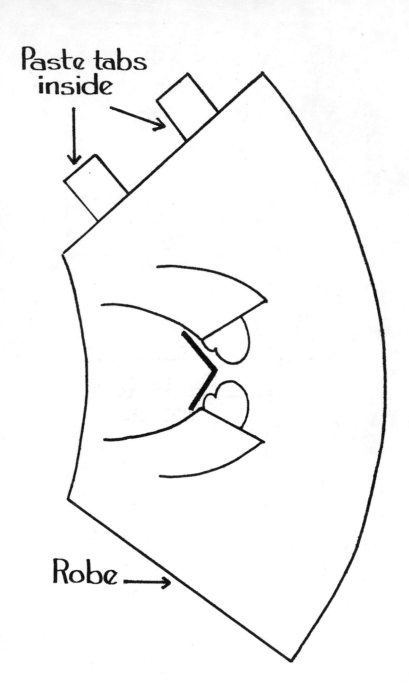

Paste tabs
inside

Robe →

Bow

Paste tab inside

Paste tab inside

Book

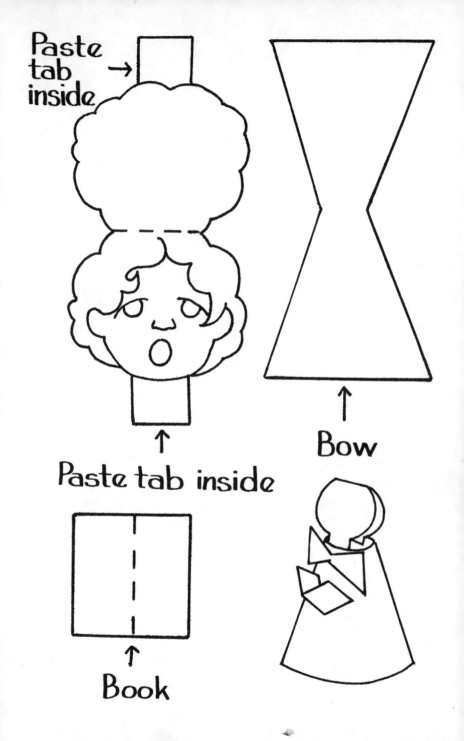

Paste
tab
inside →

Paste tab inside

Bow

Book

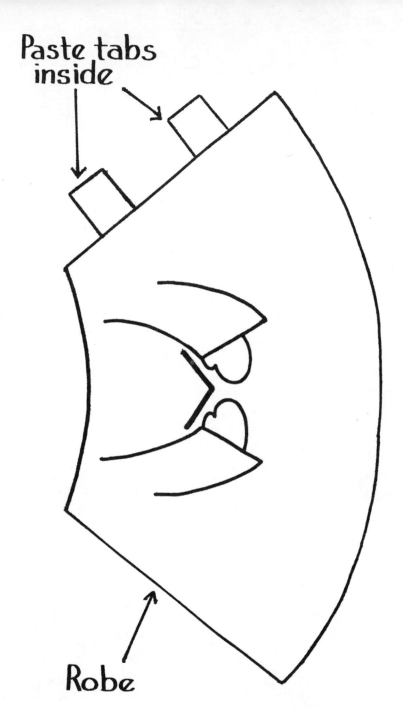

Paste tabs
inside

Robe